Key Stage 2

Fractions

Hilary Koll and Steve Mills

Name _____

Schofield & Sims

Fractions are used every day when we want to describe parts of whole things – quarter of an hour, half of a cake, or a third of the class. In this book you will find information about how to recognise and write fractions. You will practise working with fractions, and so build a better understanding of them.

How to use this book

Before you start using this book, write your name in the name box on the first page.

Then decide how to begin. If you want a complete course on fractions, you should work right through the book from beginning to end. Another way to use the book is to dip into it when you want to find out about a particular topic, such as simplifying fractions. The Contents page will help you to find the pages you need.

Whichever way you choose, don't try to do too much at once – it's better to work through the book in short bursts.

When you have found the topic you want to study, look out for these icons, which mark different parts of the text.

This icon shows you the activities that you should complete. You write your answers in the spaces provided. You might find it useful to have some spare paper to work on for some of the activities. After you have worked through all the activities on the page, turn to pages 45–49 at the end of the book to check your answers. When you are sure that you understand the topic, put a tick in the box beside it on the Contents page.

On pages 12, 22, 30 and 36 you will find **Progress tests**. These contain questions that will check your understanding of the topics that you have worked through so far. Check your answers on page 50. It is important that you correct any mistakes before moving on to the next section.

On pages 41–44 you will find a **Final test**. This will check your understanding of all the topics. Check your answers on page 51.

This text explains the topic and gives examples. Make sure you read it before you start the activities.

This text gives you useful background information about the subject.

Contents

How fractions are written

Explanation

Fractions help to describe **parts** of whole things. They are written using a **numerator** and a **denominator**.

Fractions have one number on top of another.

The number on the **bottom** is the **denominator**. ⟶ $\frac{3}{5}$

These fractions are related: they all have a denominator of **5**. ⟶ $\frac{4}{5}$ $\frac{1}{5}$ $\frac{5}{5}$ $\frac{9}{5}$

Fractions with a denominator of **5** are parts of something that have been split into **five equal parts**.

Example

a whole shape	a whole set of items	a whole pound	a whole line
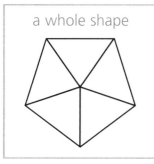	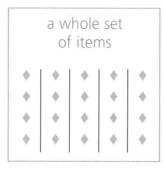		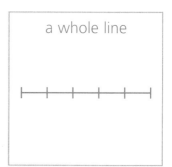

Each part here is called a **fifth** and is written $\frac{1}{5}$

The number on the **top** of your fraction is called the **numerator**. ⟶ $\frac{3}{5}$

The **numerator** shows how many of the equal parts you have.

$\frac{1}{5}$ means **1** out of **5** equal parts

$\frac{3}{5}$ means **3** out of **5** equal parts

$\frac{5}{5}$ means **5** out of **5** equal parts

Did you know?

Historians think that the Ancient Egyptians invented fractions. People needed to measure lots of things, such as the lengths of fields and the sizes of stones used to build the Pyramids. Sometimes the things they measured weren't quite the same size as their measuring sticks. They began to measure half the measuring stick or a quarter of the measuring stick, and so fractions were born.

Unit fractions of shapes

Activities

1   What fraction of each shape is shaded?

a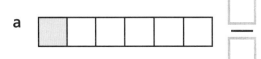

b 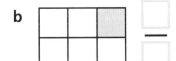   c    d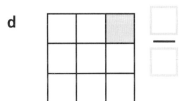

e 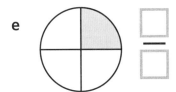   f    g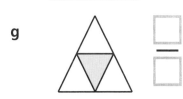

2   Colour these fractions.

a 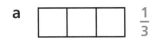 $\frac{1}{3}$

b 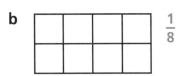 $\frac{1}{8}$

c  $\frac{1}{5}$

3   **Tick** the fractions shaded that are **correctly** named, and **cross** any that are **incorrectly** named.

a 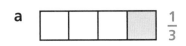 $\frac{1}{3}$

b $\frac{1}{5}$

c $\frac{1}{6}$

d  $\frac{1}{5}$

e  $\frac{1}{2}$

f 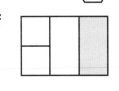 $\frac{1}{3}$

Unit fractions of numbers

Explanation

You can also find **unit fractions of numbers**. Remember that unit fractions always have a numerator of **1**, like $\frac{1}{2}$, $\frac{1}{4}$, $\frac{1}{8}$ and $\frac{1}{10}$.

To find a unit fraction of a number, split the number into equal parts or groups by dividing by the bottom number (the denominator).

Did you know?

The Ancient Egyptians only used unit fractions. These days, we use fractions that are several parts of a whole (with numerators that are numbers more than **1**), like $\frac{2}{3}$, $\frac{3}{4}$, $\frac{6}{8}$. Find out more about them on the next page.

Example $\frac{1}{5}$ of 10

Split **10** into **5** equal parts.

$10 \div 5 = 2$

It's just like division, so finding $\frac{1}{5}$ of **10** is the same as dividing **10** by 5. $\frac{1}{5}$ of 10 = 2

Activities

1 Share the buttons into equal groups to answer the questions.

a $\frac{1}{2}$ of 8

b $\frac{1}{3}$ of 9

_____

_____

2 Divide the number by the **denominator** to answer these.

a $\frac{1}{6}$ of 18 = _____

b $\frac{1}{10}$ of 50 = _____

c $\frac{1}{3}$ of 15 = _____

d $\frac{1}{5}$ of 20 = _____

3 Answer these questions mentally.

a A man earned £**60**. He gave **one-tenth** to charity. How much did he give?

b **One-quarter** of a class of **24** children is boys. How many are boys?

c There are **100** pages in a book. **One-fifth** of the pages contain pictures. How many pages contain pictures?

d **One-eighth** of the children in a school have packed lunch. There are **160** children in the school. How many have packed lunch?

Fractions

Fractions that are several parts of a whole

Explanation

Finding other fractions of shapes

- Count the number of equal parts in each shape. This is the **denominator** of the fraction.

- Count how many of these equal parts are shaded. This is the **numerator** of the fraction.

Example

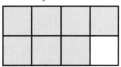

$\frac{7}{8}$ of this shape is shaded.

Activities

1 What fraction of each shape is shaded?

a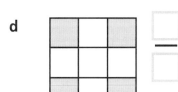

b 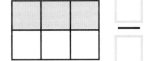 c 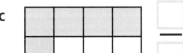   d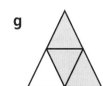

e 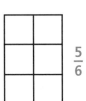 f    g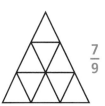

2 Shade each shape to show the fraction given.

a 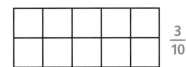 $\frac{5}{6}$ b  $\frac{2}{7}$ c $\frac{7}{9}$

d 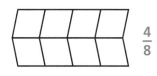 $\frac{3}{10}$ e  $\frac{2}{5}$ f $\frac{4}{8}$

3 Tick the pictures that show $\frac{3}{5}$.

a   b 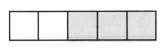 c   d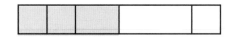

Fractions of sets

Explanation

- Count the number of counters below. This is the **denominator**.
- Count the number of counters that are shaded. This is the **numerator**.

Example What fraction of these counters is shaded?

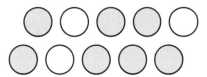

Seven out of ten objects are shaded, so $\frac{7}{10}$ of the counters is shaded.

Activities

1 What fraction of these objects is shaded?

a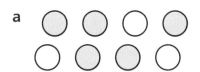

b

c

d

e

f

2 Shade some of each set to show the fraction given.

a  $\frac{3}{7}$

b  $\frac{7}{8}$

c  $\frac{5}{10}$

d  $\frac{5}{6}$

3 Tick the pictures that show $\frac{2}{5}$.

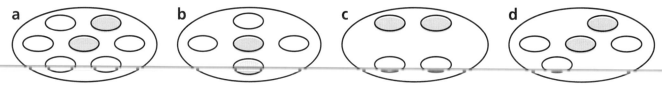

a b c d

Mixed numbers

Explanation

Numbers like $3\frac{1}{2}$, $4\frac{1}{4}$ and $6\frac{3}{4}$ are called **mixed numbers** because they are a mix of whole numbers such as **3**, **4** and **6** and fractions such as $\frac{1}{2}$, $\frac{1}{4}$ and $\frac{3}{4}$.

Example $3\frac{1}{4}$ glasses of water

Activities

1 Match the **mixed numbers** to the correct pictures.

 $1\frac{3}{4}$

 $2\frac{1}{4}$

 $2\frac{1}{2}$

 $3\frac{1}{4}$

 $3\frac{1}{2}$

 $4\frac{1}{3}$

 $4\frac{7}{10}$

$5\frac{3}{10}$

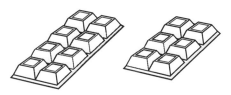

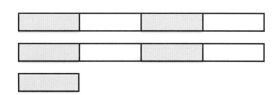

2 Continue these patterns.

a $\frac{1}{2}$ 1 $1\frac{1}{2}$ 2 $2\frac{1}{2}$ ____ ____ ____ ____ ____

b $\frac{1}{4}$ $\frac{2}{4}$ $\frac{3}{4}$ 1 $1\frac{1}{4}$ ____ ____ ____ ____ ____

c $3\frac{1}{3}$ $3\frac{2}{3}$ 4 $4\frac{1}{3}$ ____ ____ ____ ____ ____

d $\frac{1}{5}$ $\frac{2}{5}$ $\frac{3}{5}$ $\frac{4}{5}$ 1 $1\frac{1}{5}$ ____ ____ ____ ____ ____

Explanation

Equivalent fractions are fractions that stand for the same amount.

They can look very different but are actually worth the same.

Example

$$\frac{2}{4} \quad \text{and} \quad \frac{1}{2}$$

$$\frac{2}{3} \quad \text{and} \quad \frac{4}{6} \quad \text{and} \quad \frac{6}{9}$$

Activities

1 A fraction of each flag is shaded. Join any flags that show the same fraction.

2 Write the fraction that is shaded in each rectangle. Join any **equivalent fractions**.

Finding fractions of numbers

On page 6 you learnt how to find **unit fractions** of numbers, like $\frac{1}{3}$ of **12** and $\frac{1}{6}$ of **18**. Unit fractions always have a numerator of **1**.

Example To find $\frac{1}{6}$ of **18** we divide **18** by **6** $18 \div 6 = 3$ so $\frac{1}{6}$ of **18** = **3**

Once you can find a unit fraction of a number, you can find **any** fraction of a number by multiplying, as shown below.

Example Find $\frac{3}{5}$ of **10**.

First find $\frac{1}{5}$ of **10**.   **one**-fifth of **10** = **10** ÷ **5** = **2**

Then **multiply** by the number of fifths (the numerator) in the question.

one-fifth of **10** = **2**   so **three**-fifths of **10** = **3** × **2** = **6**

Always **find the unit fraction first**, then **multiply** to find other fractions.

Example $\frac{5}{8}$ of **32** $32 \div 8 = 4$ $5 \times 4 = 20$

one-eighth of **32**   five-eighths of **32**

Activities

1   Find:

    a $\frac{2}{3}$ of **12** _____   **b** $\frac{2}{3}$ of **18** _____   **c** $\frac{3}{4}$ of **16** _____   **d** $\frac{3}{4}$ of **20** _____

2   Find:

    a $\frac{3}{8}$ of **16** _____   **b** $\frac{3}{8}$ of **24** _____   **c** $\frac{7}{8}$ of **32** _____   **d** $\frac{5}{8}$ of **40** _____

    e $\frac{3}{4}$ of **40** _____   **f** $\frac{5}{6}$ of **36** _____   **g** $\frac{7}{9}$ of **27** _____   **h** $\frac{7}{10}$ of **80** _____

3   Find three-quarters of:

    a 24 _____   **b** 32 _____   **c** 48 _____   **d** 60 _____

4   Find four-fifths of:

    a 30 _____   **b** 40 _____   **c** 25 _____   **d** 45 _____

5   Dylan spent these fractions of one day (24 hours) on four different activities. How many hours did he spend on each?

    a $\frac{3}{12}$ _____   **b** $\frac{5}{24}$ _____   **c** $\frac{3}{8}$ _____   **d** $\frac{1}{6}$ _____

1 What fraction of each shape is shaded?   **a**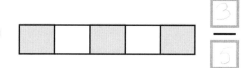

b 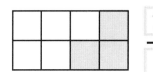   **c**    **d**

2 Divide the number by the denominator to answer these.

a $\frac{1}{6}$ of **24** = _____ 4

b $\frac{1}{10}$ of **30** = _____ 3

c $\frac{1}{3}$ of **12** = _____

d $\frac{1}{5}$ of **25** = _____

3 Answer these questions mentally.

a
> A man earned **£40**. He gave
> **one-tenth** to charity.
> How much did he give?

b
> **One-quarter** of a class of
> **36** children is girls.
> How many are girls?

c
> There are **50** pages in a book.
> **One-fifth** of the pages contain
> pictures. How many pages
> contain pictures?

d
> **One-eighth** of the children in a school
> have packed lunch. There are
> **240** children in the school.
> How many have packed lunch?

4 Shade objects in each set to show each fraction.

a $\frac{3}{5}$    **b** $\frac{5}{8}$    **c** $\frac{1}{10}$

5 Count on or back in equal steps to continue the sequences.

a $2\frac{1}{2}$ 3 $3\frac{1}{2}$ 4   ___ ___ ___ ___ ___

b $4\frac{1}{2}$ $4\frac{3}{4}$ 5 $5\frac{1}{4}$ ___ ___ ___ ___ ___

c $9\frac{1}{4}$ 9 $8\frac{3}{4}$ $8\frac{1}{2}$ ___ ___ ___ ___ ___

6 Work these out.

a $\frac{3}{8}$ of **32**   **b** $\frac{5}{6}$ of **24**   **c** $\frac{2}{9}$ of **45**

Tenths

Explanation

Measurements are often split into **10** equal pieces called **tenths**. For example, a centimetre is split into 10 equal parts called millimetres. One millimetre is **one-tenth** or $\frac{1}{10}$ of a centimetre.

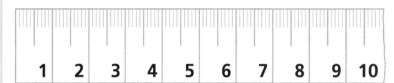

Fractions greater than one whole can be written as mixed numbers such as $1\frac{1}{10}$ or as improper (top-heavy) fractions such as $\frac{11}{10}$.

Activities

1 Count on in tenths.

a $\frac{1}{10}, \frac{2}{10}, \frac{3}{10}, \frac{4}{10}, \underline{\phantom{\frac{}{10}}}, \underline{\phantom{\frac{}{10}}}, \frac{7}{10}, \underline{\phantom{\frac{}{10}}}, \frac{9}{10}, \frac{10}{10}, \frac{11}{10}, \frac{12}{10}, \underline{\phantom{\frac{}{10}}}, \underline{\phantom{\frac{}{10}}}, \frac{15}{10} \cdots$

b $\frac{8}{10}, \frac{9}{10}, 1, 1\frac{1}{10}, 1\frac{2}{10}, \square, \square, 1\frac{5}{10}, \square, \square, \square, \square, \square \cdots$

When a whole number is divided by **10** the answer can be written as a fraction.

Example $3 \div 10 = \frac{3}{10}$ $7 \div 10 = \frac{7}{10}$

Some answers can be written as simpler equivalent fractions.

Example $5 \div 10 = \frac{5}{10} = \frac{1}{2}$

---

2 Divide each number by **10** and write your answers as fractions with the denominator **10**.

a $1 \div 10 = \dfrac{\square}{\square}$ **b** $9 \div 10 = \dfrac{\square}{\square}$ **c** $6 \div 10 = \dfrac{\square}{\square}$

d $2 \div 10 = \dfrac{\square}{\square}$ **e** $4 \div 10 = \dfrac{\square}{\square}$ **f** $8 \div 10 = \dfrac{\square}{\square}$

3 Can you write any of your answers as equivalent fractions?

Explanation

You may remember that fractions are equal parts of things.

$\frac{3}{4}$ means something is split into four equal parts and you have three of the parts. If you get one more part you will have the whole thing.

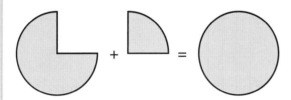

Three-quarters plus one-quarter makes four-quarters and four-quarters is the same as one whole.

$\frac{3}{4} + \frac{1}{4} = \frac{4}{4}$ and $\frac{4}{4}$ is the same as **1** whole.

In the same way $\frac{1}{3} + \frac{2}{3} = $ **1** and $\frac{2}{7} + \frac{5}{7} = $ **1**.

Activities

1 Find pairs of fractions with a total of **one** from the grid and write them below.

$\frac{2}{3}$	$\frac{1}{6}$	$\frac{5}{8}$	$\frac{1}{2}$
$\frac{1}{7}$	$\frac{1}{4}$	$\frac{3}{7}$	$\frac{3}{10}$
$\frac{9}{10}$	$\frac{7}{8}$	$\frac{3}{8}$	$\frac{3}{4}$
$\frac{6}{7}$	$\frac{1}{9}$	$\frac{4}{9}$	$\frac{2}{5}$
$\frac{7}{10}$	$\frac{1}{5}$	$\frac{1}{3}$	$\frac{1}{2}$
$\frac{5}{9}$	$\frac{3}{5}$	$\frac{5}{6}$	$\frac{4}{5}$
$\frac{1}{8}$	$\frac{4}{7}$	$\frac{1}{10}$	$\frac{8}{9}$

$\frac{2}{3} + \frac{1}{3} = 1$ $\qquad$ $\frac{\square}{\square} + \frac{\square}{\square} = 1$

$\frac{\square}{\square} + \frac{\square}{\square} = 1$ $\qquad$ $\frac{\square}{\square} + \frac{\square}{\square} = 1$

$\frac{\square}{\square} + \frac{\square}{\square} = 1$ $\qquad$ $\frac{\square}{\square} + \frac{\square}{\square} = 1$

$\frac{\square}{\square} + \frac{\square}{\square} = 1$ $\qquad$ $\frac{\square}{\square} + \frac{\square}{\square} = 1$

$\frac{\square}{\square} + \frac{\square}{\square} = 1$ $\qquad$ $\frac{\square}{\square} + \frac{\square}{\square} = 1$

$\frac{\square}{\square} + \frac{\square}{\square} = 1$ $\qquad$ $\frac{\square}{\square} + \frac{\square}{\square} = 1$

$\frac{\square}{\square} + \frac{\square}{\square} = 1$ $\qquad$ $\frac{\square}{\square} + \frac{\square}{\square} = 1$

Adding fractions with the same denominators

Explanation

On page 14 you added fractions together that had a total of **one**. You can add other fractions with the **same denominators** in a similar way.

Some answers will be less than one.

Example

Example $\frac{3}{10} + \frac{4}{10} = \frac{7}{10}$

 + 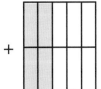 =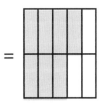

Some answers will be greater than one. The answers can be given as an improper (top-heavy) fraction or as a mixed number.

$$\frac{8}{10} + \frac{9}{10} = \frac{17}{10} = 1\frac{7}{10}$$

Remember not to add the denominators.

Activities

1 Add these fractions.

a $\frac{3}{9} + \frac{4}{9} =$ _____

b $\frac{2}{8} + \frac{5}{8} =$ _____

c $\frac{1}{10} + \frac{8}{10} =$ _____

d $\frac{4}{7} + \frac{1}{7} =$ _____

2 Add these fractions and give your answers as improper (top-heavy) fractions.

a $\frac{6}{10} + \frac{7}{10} =$ _____

b $\frac{4}{9} + \frac{8}{9} =$ _____

c $\frac{5}{7} + \frac{5}{7} =$ _____

d $\frac{3}{8} + \frac{7}{8} =$ _____

3 Add these fractions and give your answers as mixed numbers.

a $\frac{3}{4} + \frac{2}{4} =$ _____

b $\frac{3}{5} + \frac{4}{5} =$ _____

c $\frac{8}{10} + \frac{5}{10} =$ _____

d $\frac{7}{9} + \frac{8}{9} =$ _____

e $\frac{7}{10} + \frac{7}{10} + \frac{9}{10} =$ _____

f $\frac{5}{6} + \frac{5}{6} + \frac{1}{6} =$ _____

Subtracting fractions with the same denominators

Explanation

Subtracting fractions with the **same denominators** is very similar.

Example

$\frac{9}{10} - \frac{2}{10} = \frac{7}{10}$

 − =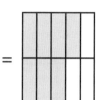

If the first number in the subtraction is an improper (top-heavy) fraction, just subtract in the same way.

Example $\frac{11}{10} - \frac{5}{10} = \frac{6}{10}$ $\qquad \frac{20}{8} - \frac{6}{8} = \frac{14}{8} = 1\frac{6}{8}$

Remember not to subtract the denominators.

Activities

1 Subtract these fractions.

a $\frac{8}{9} - \frac{1}{9} =$ _____

b $\frac{7}{8} - \frac{5}{8} =$ _____

c $\frac{9}{10} - \frac{3}{10} =$ _____

d $\frac{7}{7} - \frac{3}{7} =$ _____

2 Subtract these fractions, giving your answers as improper fractions.

a $\frac{11}{7} - \frac{3}{7} =$ _____

b $\frac{16}{5} - \frac{4}{5} =$ _____

c $\frac{14}{10} - \frac{1}{10} =$ _____

d $\frac{20}{6} - \frac{1}{6} =$ _____

3 Subtract these fractions, giving your answers as mixed numbers.

a $\frac{8}{4} - \frac{3}{4} =$ _____

b $\frac{13}{5} - \frac{4}{5} =$ _____

c $\frac{19}{10} - \frac{2}{10} =$ _____

d $\frac{20}{7} - \frac{9}{7} =$ _____

Comparing and ordering unit fractions

Fractions are unusual because the larger the **denominator** (the bottom number), the smaller the fraction.

Example If you were offered $\frac{1}{8}$ or $\frac{1}{3}$ of a pizza, which is larger and which is smaller?

You might think that, because **8** is larger than **3**, $\frac{1}{8}$ is larger than $\frac{1}{3}$, but this is not the case. Look at these pictures.

$\frac{1}{8} < \frac{1}{3}$

Activities

1 Compare these fractions, writing < or > between them to show which is larger.

a $\frac{1}{4}$ _____ $\frac{1}{5}$ b $\frac{1}{9}$ _____ $\frac{1}{2}$ c $\frac{1}{8}$ _____ $\frac{1}{10}$

d $\frac{1}{6}$ _____ $\frac{1}{3}$ e $\frac{1}{5}$ _____ $\frac{1}{10}$ f $\frac{1}{2}$ _____ $\frac{1}{7}$

2 Order these fractions, starting with the smallest.

a $\frac{1}{2}$ $\frac{1}{8}$ $\frac{1}{5}$ _____ b $\frac{1}{3}$ $\frac{1}{9}$ $\frac{1}{10}$ _____

c $\frac{1}{4}$ $\frac{1}{3}$ $\frac{1}{9}$ _____ d $\frac{1}{6}$ $\frac{1}{10}$ $\frac{1}{8}$ _____

3 Order these fractions, starting with the largest.

a $\frac{1}{7}$ $\frac{1}{6}$ $\frac{1}{9}$ $\frac{1}{4}$ _____

b $\frac{1}{10}$ $\frac{1}{2}$ $\frac{1}{7}$ $\frac{1}{5}$ _____

c $\frac{1}{5}$ $\frac{1}{9}$ $\frac{1}{2}$ $\frac{1}{4}$ _____

Ordering fractions

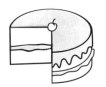 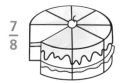
Activities

1 Compare these fractions, writing < or > between them to show which is larger.

a $\frac{5}{6}$ _____ $\frac{1}{6}$

b $\frac{6}{9}$ _____ $\frac{7}{9}$

c $\frac{5}{8}$ _____ $\frac{3}{8}$

d $\frac{3}{5}$ _____ $\frac{4}{5}$

e $\frac{7}{10}$ _____ $\frac{5}{10}$

f $\frac{4}{7}$ _____ $\frac{1}{7}$

2 Order these fractions, smallest first.

a $\frac{4}{5}$ $\frac{3}{5}$ $\frac{1}{5}$ _____

b $\frac{1}{8}$ $\frac{3}{8}$ $\frac{6}{8}$ _____

c $\frac{4}{9}$ $\frac{7}{9}$ $\frac{6}{9}$ _____

d $\frac{2}{10}$ $\frac{1}{10}$ $\frac{9}{10}$ _____

3 Order these fractions, largest first.

a $\frac{5}{12}$ $\frac{7}{12}$ $\frac{9}{12}$ $\frac{3}{12}$ _____

b $\frac{7}{10}$ $\frac{4}{10}$ $\frac{5}{10}$ $\frac{3}{10}$ _____

c $\frac{1}{8}$ $\frac{4}{8}$ $\frac{2}{8}$ $\frac{6}{8}$ _____

Equivalent fractions 2

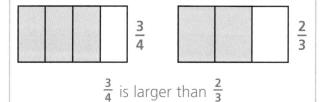
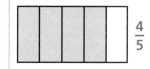 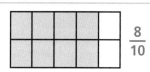
Activities

1 Shade the two fractions in each pair. Circle the largest fraction in each pair, or write **=** in the box if they are equivalent.

a  $\frac{3}{4}$ □
$\frac{7}{8}$

b $\frac{1}{5}$ □
$\frac{1}{4}$

c $\frac{2}{5}$ □
$\frac{4}{10}$

d $\frac{3}{4}$ □
$\frac{5}{6}$

e $\frac{2}{3}$ □
$\frac{6}{8}$

f  $\frac{3}{5}$ □
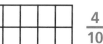 $\frac{9}{15}$

2 Write the fractions for each diagram to reveal pairs of equivalent fractions.

a  □
—
□

b □
—
□

c  □
—
□

d 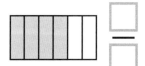 □
—
□

e  □
—
□

f 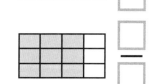 □
—
□

Explanation

A fraction wall is sometimes useful as it can help you to compare fractions or find equivalent fractions. Use a straight edge, like this dotted line for example, to help you see that $\frac{1}{3}$ is equivalent to $\frac{4}{12}$.

Example $\frac{1}{3} = \frac{4}{12}$

1											
$\frac{1}{2}$						$\frac{1}{2}$					
$\frac{1}{3}$				$\frac{1}{3}$				$\frac{1}{3}$			
$\frac{1}{4}$			$\frac{1}{4}$			$\frac{1}{4}$			$\frac{1}{4}$		
$\frac{1}{5}$		$\frac{1}{5}$		$\frac{1}{5}$		$\frac{1}{5}$		$\frac{1}{5}$			
$\frac{1}{6}$		$\frac{1}{6}$		$\frac{1}{6}$		$\frac{1}{6}$		$\frac{1}{6}$		$\frac{1}{6}$	
$\frac{1}{7}$	$\frac{1}{7}$		$\frac{1}{7}$		$\frac{1}{7}$		$\frac{1}{7}$		$\frac{1}{7}$		$\frac{1}{7}$
$\frac{1}{8}$	$\frac{1}{8}$		$\frac{1}{8}$	$\frac{1}{8}$		$\frac{1}{8}$	$\frac{1}{8}$		$\frac{1}{8}$		$\frac{1}{8}$
$\frac{1}{9}$	$\frac{1}{9}$	$\frac{1}{9}$	$\frac{1}{9}$	$\frac{1}{9}$	$\frac{1}{9}$	$\frac{1}{9}$	$\frac{1}{9}$	$\frac{1}{9}$			
$\frac{1}{10}$	$\frac{1}{10}$	$\frac{1}{10}$	$\frac{1}{10}$	$\frac{1}{10}$	$\frac{1}{10}$	$\frac{1}{10}$	$\frac{1}{10}$	$\frac{1}{10}$	$\frac{1}{10}$		
$\frac{1}{11}$	$\frac{1}{11}$	$\frac{1}{11}$	$\frac{1}{11}$	$\frac{1}{11}$	$\frac{1}{11}$	$\frac{1}{11}$	$\frac{1}{11}$	$\frac{1}{11}$	$\frac{1}{11}$	$\frac{1}{11}$	
$\frac{1}{12}$	$\frac{1}{12}$	$\frac{1}{12}$	$\frac{1}{12}$	$\frac{1}{12}$	$\frac{1}{12}$	$\frac{1}{12}$	$\frac{1}{12}$	$\frac{1}{12}$	$\frac{1}{12}$	$\frac{1}{12}$	$\frac{1}{12}$

Activities

1 Compare these fractions, writing <, > or = between them.

a $\frac{2}{12}$ _____ $\frac{1}{6}$ b $\frac{2}{5}$ _____ $\frac{1}{4}$ c $\frac{2}{6}$ _____ $\frac{1}{3}$

d $\frac{2}{8}$ _____ $\frac{1}{5}$ e $\frac{3}{12}$ _____ $\frac{1}{4}$ f $\frac{6}{8}$ _____ $\frac{3}{4}$

g $\frac{2}{10}$ _____ $\frac{1}{5}$ h $\frac{6}{10}$ _____ $\frac{3}{5}$ i $\frac{9}{12}$ _____ $\frac{3}{4}$

Hundredths

Explanation

Measurements are often split into **100** equal pieces called **hundredths**. For example, a metre is split into 100 equal parts called centimetres. One centimetre is **one-hundredth** or $\frac{1}{100}$ of a metre.

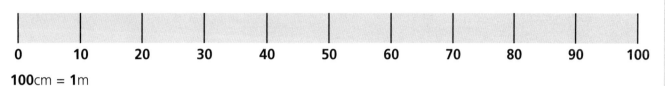

100cm = **1**m

Activities

1 Count on in hundredths.

a $\frac{1}{100}$, $\frac{2}{100}$, $\frac{3}{100}$, $\frac{4}{100}$, $\frac{}{100}$, $\frac{}{100}$, $\frac{}{100}$, $\frac{}{100}$, $\frac{}{100}$, $\frac{10}{100}$, $\frac{11}{100}$, $\frac{}{100}$, $\frac{}{100}$ ...

b $\frac{46}{100}$, $\frac{47}{100}$, $\frac{48}{100}$, $\frac{}{100}$, $\frac{}{100}$, $\frac{}{100}$, $\frac{}{100}$, $\frac{}{100}$, $\frac{54}{100}$, $\frac{55}{100}$, $\frac{}{100}$, $\frac{}{100}$ ...

c $\frac{98}{100}$, $\frac{99}{100}$, 1, $1\frac{1}{100}$, ☐, ☐, $1\frac{4}{100}$, ☐, ☐, ☐, ☐, ☐ ...

When a whole number is divided by **100** the answer can be written as a fraction.

Example $3 \div 100 = \frac{3}{100}$ $27 \div 100 = \frac{27}{100}$

Some answers can be written as simpler **equivalent fractions**.

Example $25 \div 100 = \frac{25}{100} = \frac{1}{4}$

---

2 Divide each number by **100** and write your answers as fractions with the denominator **100**.

a $1 \div 100 = \frac{\boxed{}}{\boxed{}}$ **b** $29 \div 100 = \frac{\boxed{}}{\boxed{}}$ **c** $9 \div 100 = \frac{\boxed{}}{\boxed{}}$

d $70 \div 100 = \frac{\boxed{}}{\boxed{}}$ **e** $75 \div 100 = \frac{\boxed{}}{\boxed{}}$ **f** $50 \div 100 = \frac{\boxed{}}{\boxed{}}$

3 Can you write any of your answers as equivalent fractions?

_____

Progress test 2

1 Write your answers to these divisions, giving a fraction with the denominator **10**.

a $7 \div 10 =$ _____

b $9 \div 10 =$ _____

c $11 \div 10 =$ _____

2 Fill in the missing fractions.

a $\dfrac{3}{8} + \dfrac{\square}{\square} = 1$

b $\dfrac{2}{5} + \dfrac{\square}{\square} = 1$

c $\dfrac{\square}{\square} + \dfrac{5}{9} = 1$

d $\dfrac{\square}{\square} + \dfrac{7}{12} = 1$

3 Add or subtract these fractions, giving your answers as mixed numbers.

a $\dfrac{9}{10} + \dfrac{4}{10} =$ _____

b $\dfrac{16}{9} - \dfrac{2}{9} =$ _____

c $\dfrac{7}{10} + \dfrac{7}{10} + \dfrac{7}{10} =$ _____

d $\dfrac{27}{8} - \dfrac{2}{8} =$ _____

4 Order these fractions, smallest first.

a $\dfrac{1}{2}$ $\dfrac{1}{8}$ $\dfrac{1}{4}$ _____

b $\dfrac{2}{12}$ $\dfrac{1}{12}$ $\dfrac{9}{12}$ _____

5 Write the fraction of each rectangle that is shaded. Join any equivalent fractions.

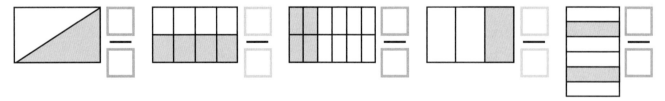

6 Count on in hundredths.

$\dfrac{75}{100}$, $\dfrac{76}{100}$, $\dfrac{77}{100}$, $\dfrac{78}{100}$, $\dfrac{}{100}$, $\dfrac{}{100}$, $\dfrac{}{100}$, $\dfrac{}{100}$, $\dfrac{83}{100}$, $\dfrac{84}{100}$, $\dfrac{}{100}$, $\dfrac{}{100}$ ...

7 Write your answers to these divisions, giving a fraction with the denominator **100**.

a $7 \div 100 =$ _____

b $51 \div 100 =$ _____

c $273 \div 100 =$ _____

Fractions

Explanation

On page 11 you learnt how to find a fraction of a number or quantity – dividing by the **denominator** to find one part and multiplying by the **numerator** to find several parts.

Example $\frac{3}{5}$ of **10**   first find **one**-fifth of **10** $\longrightarrow$ $10 \div 5 = 2$
then find **three**-fifths of **10** $\longrightarrow$ $2 \times 3 = 6$

If possible, simplify the fraction to a simple **equivalent fraction** to make the multiplication and division easier.

$\frac{9}{18}$ of **46**   Rather than dividing **18** by **46** and then multiplying the answer by **9**, notice that $\frac{9}{18}$ is equivalent to $\frac{1}{2}$ and do the question $\frac{1}{2}$ of **46** instead.

Look back at the fraction wall on page 20 to help you simplify your answer if you need to.

Activities

1 Simplify the fraction first to help you answer the question in your head.

a $\boxed{\dfrac{2}{8}}$ of **20** = $\dfrac{\square}{\square}$ of **20** = _____

b $\boxed{\dfrac{3}{6}}$ of **22** = $\dfrac{\square}{\square}$ of **22** = _____

c $\boxed{\dfrac{8}{10}}$ of **25** = $\dfrac{\square}{\square}$ of **25** = _____

d $\boxed{\dfrac{9}{12}}$ of **40** = $\dfrac{\square}{\square}$ of **40** = _____

e $\boxed{\dfrac{6}{9}}$ of **30** = $\dfrac{\square}{\square}$ of **30** = _____

f $\boxed{\dfrac{6}{10}}$ of **35** = $\dfrac{\square}{\square}$ of **35** = _____

2 Use this number line to help you simplify hundredths to tenths first.

| 0 | $\frac{10}{100}$ | $\frac{20}{100}$ | $\frac{30}{100}$ | $\frac{40}{100}$ | $\frac{50}{100}$ | $\frac{60}{100}$ | $\frac{70}{100}$ | $\frac{80}{100}$ | $\frac{90}{100}$ | 1 |

| 0 | $\frac{1}{10}$ | $\frac{2}{10}$ | $\frac{3}{10}$ | $\frac{4}{10}$ | $\frac{5}{10}$ | $\frac{6}{10}$ | $\frac{7}{10}$ | $\frac{8}{10}$ | $\frac{9}{10}$ | 1 |

a $\boxed{\dfrac{70}{100}}$ of **30** = $\dfrac{\square}{\square}$ of **30** = _____

b $\boxed{\dfrac{90}{100}}$ of **20** = $\dfrac{\square}{\square}$ of **20** = _____

c $\boxed{\dfrac{30}{100}}$ of **90** = $\dfrac{\square}{\square}$ of **90** = _____

d $\boxed{\dfrac{70}{100}}$ of **120** = $\dfrac{\square}{\square}$ of **120** = _____

Fractions on a number line

Explanation

Fractions and mixed numbers lie between whole numbers.

Here are some that lie between **3** and **4**.

3      $3\frac{1}{4}$ $3\frac{2}{5}$ $3\frac{1}{2}$ $3\frac{3}{5}$ $3\frac{3}{4}$ 4

There are an infinite number of fractions and mixed numbers between any two whole numbers.

You can mark fractions on a number line between two whole numbers by splitting the line into equal parts. The denominator tells you how many parts to split the line into. You can mark $\frac{1}{3}$ and $\frac{2}{3}$ on this line by splitting the line into thirds.

$$0 \qquad\qquad \frac{1}{3} \qquad\qquad \frac{2}{3} \qquad\qquad 1$$

Activities

1   Join each fraction to its correct position on the line.

a

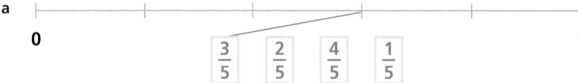

$\frac{3}{5}$ $\frac{2}{5}$ $\frac{4}{5}$ $\frac{1}{5}$

b

$\frac{3}{8}$ $\frac{1}{2}$ $\frac{5}{8}$ $\frac{7}{8}$ $\frac{1}{8}$

c

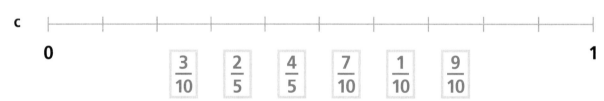

$\frac{3}{10}$ $\frac{2}{5}$ $\frac{4}{5}$ $\frac{7}{10}$ $\frac{1}{10}$ $\frac{9}{10}$

2   Write the fractions that the arrows are pointing to. Think about equivalent fractions!

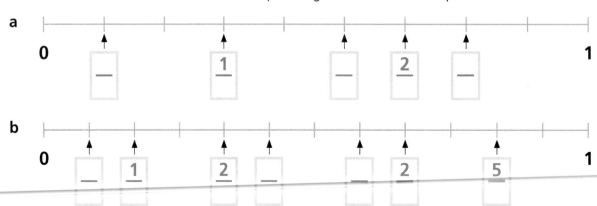

Equivalent fractions 3

Explanation

Do you remember that equivalent fractions have the same value but are made using different digits?

All of the fractions below are **equivalent** to one-half.

$\dfrac{2}{4}$

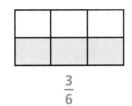

$\dfrac{3}{6}$

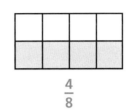

$\dfrac{4}{8}$

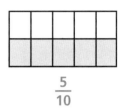

$\dfrac{5}{10}$

To find fractions that are **equivalent**, you can **multiply** or **divide** the top and bottom numbers by the same number.

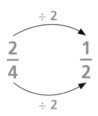

$\div 2$

$\dfrac{2}{4} \quad \dfrac{1}{2}$

$\div 2$

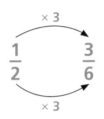

$\times 3$

$\dfrac{1}{2} \quad \dfrac{3}{6}$

$\times 3$

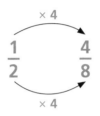

$\times 4$

$\dfrac{1}{2} \quad \dfrac{4}{8}$

$\times 4$

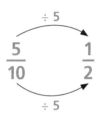

$\div 5$

$\dfrac{5}{10} \quad \dfrac{1}{2}$

$\div 5$

These fractions are all **equivalent** to one-half.

Activities

1 Find eight sets of equivalent fractions. Write them below.

$\dfrac{1}{2}$	$\dfrac{3}{8}$	$\dfrac{5}{6}$	$\dfrac{1}{4}$	$\dfrac{6}{16}$	$\dfrac{4}{10}$	$\dfrac{1}{3}$	$\dfrac{10}{12}$	$\dfrac{2}{8}$	$\dfrac{2}{5}$
$\dfrac{1}{5}$	$\dfrac{8}{20}$	$\dfrac{15}{18}$	$\dfrac{10}{20}$	$\dfrac{1}{7}$	$\dfrac{2}{6}$	$\dfrac{6}{12}$	$\dfrac{10}{30}$	$\dfrac{5}{15}$	$\dfrac{3}{15}$
$\dfrac{4}{20}$	$\dfrac{3}{9}$	$\dfrac{5}{10}$	$\dfrac{5}{25}$	$\dfrac{50}{100}$	$\dfrac{16}{40}$	$\dfrac{2}{10}$	$\dfrac{4}{16}$	$\dfrac{4}{12}$	$\dfrac{2}{14}$

Set **a** _____   Set **b** _____

Set **c** _____   Set **d** _____

Set **e** _____   Set **f** _____

Set **g** _____   Set **h** _____

2 Write two more equivalent fractions in each of the sets of fractions you have made above.

Simplifying fractions 2

Use a fraction wall or diagrams to simplify a fraction to make an equivalent fraction with smaller numbers. An even easier way is to divide the top and bottom numbers of the fraction by the same number.

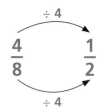 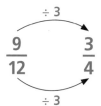 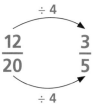

Activities

1 Divide the numerator and denominator of the fraction by the number shown to simplify each fraction.

a 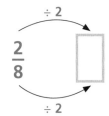 b 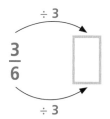 c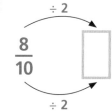

d 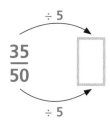 e 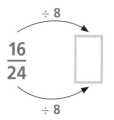 f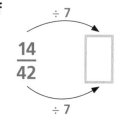

2 Decide which number to divide the numerator and denominator of the fraction by to simplify each fraction. The number needs to be a factor of both numbers (it divides into them without remainders).

a 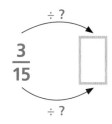 b 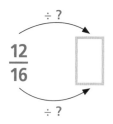 c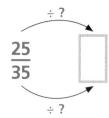

d 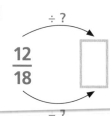 e 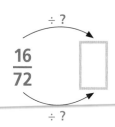 f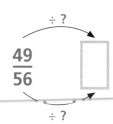

Common denominators

Explanation

On page 25 you learnt how to change fractions into **equivalent fractions** by multiplying or dividing the numerator and denominator by the same number.

Example

$\frac{9}{36}$ is equivalent to $\frac{1}{4}$ because you can **divide** the numerator and denominator by **9**.

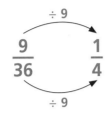

And $\frac{2}{5}$ is equivalent to $\frac{10}{25}$ because you can **multiply** each by **5**.

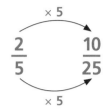

Activities

1 Write two fractions that are equivalent to each of these fractions.

a $\frac{3}{5}$ _____ _____

b $\frac{5}{8}$ _____ _____

c $\frac{6}{9}$ _____ _____

d $\frac{10}{14}$ _____ _____

e $\frac{20}{25}$ _____ _____

f $\frac{30}{100}$ _____ _____

Sometimes, if you need to compare or order fractions, you have to find equivalent fractions with a **common denominator**. This means changing one or more of the fractions so they have the same denominator.

Example Which is larger $\frac{3}{5}$ or $\frac{7}{10}$?

Change $\frac{3}{5}$ into tenths by multiplying the top and bottom by **2**.

If you then compare $\frac{6}{10}$ and $\frac{7}{10}$ it's easier to see that $\frac{7}{10}$ is larger.

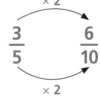

2 Change these fractions so that they have a common denominator. Circle the largest fraction in each pair.

a $\frac{2}{5}$ $\frac{3}{10}$ → ⬚ ⬚

b $\frac{1}{4}$ $\frac{3}{8}$ → ⬚ ⬚

c $\frac{5}{8}$ $\frac{11}{16}$ → ⬚ ⬚

d $\frac{2}{3}$ $\frac{5}{9}$ → ⬚ ⬚

e $\frac{3}{8}$ $\frac{11}{24}$ → ⬚ ⬚

f $\frac{4}{7}$ $\frac{11}{21}$ → ⬚ ⬚

3 Circle the largest fraction in each group.

a $\frac{2}{3}$ $\frac{7}{9}$ $\frac{13}{18}$

b $\frac{3}{4}$ $\frac{13}{16}$ $\frac{5}{8}$

c $\frac{7}{12}$ $\frac{5}{6}$ $\frac{19}{24}$

Explanation

Numbers like $3\frac{1}{2}$, $4\frac{1}{4}$ and $6\frac{3}{4}$ are called **mixed numbers** because they are a mixture of whole numbers and fractions.

In this picture, **7** quarters are shaded:

You can write this in two ways: seven-quarters $\frac{7}{4}$ or one whole and three-quarters $1\frac{3}{4}$

This is called an **improper fraction** as the **numerator** (number on top) is **larger** than the **denominator** (number on bottom).

This is called a **mixed number** because it has a whole number and a fraction.

Changing improper fractions to mixed numbers

Example Change $\frac{13}{4}$ to a mixed number.

How many lots of the denominator are in the numerator?
How many **4**s in **13**?

Find the answer and write it with a remainder.

$3\ r1$

The first number is the whole number.

The remainder tells you the numerator of the fraction.

$3\frac{1}{4}$

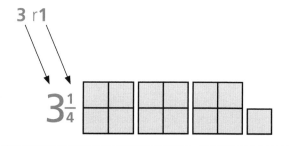

Activities

1 Change these improper fractions to mixed numbers.

a $\frac{3}{2}$ _____ b $\frac{7}{2}$ _____ c $\frac{5}{3}$ _____ d $\frac{7}{4}$ _____

e $\frac{17}{10}$ _____ f $\frac{13}{5}$ _____ g $\frac{17}{6}$ _____ h $\frac{21}{4}$ _____

i $\frac{25}{4}$ _____ j $\frac{22}{5}$ _____ k $\frac{47}{6}$ _____ l $\frac{59}{10}$ _____

Mixed numbers and improper fractions 2

Explanation

Changing mixed numbers to improper fractions

Example Change $2\frac{3}{4}$ to an improper fraction.

Look at the denominator.
You need to change this mixed number into quarters.

How many quarters are in $2\frac{3}{4}$?

There are **8** quarters in the **2** wholes and **3** quarters more.
So there are **11** quarters in $2\frac{3}{4}$.

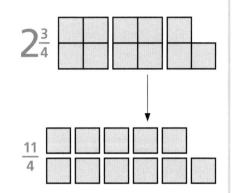

Activities

1 Change these mixed numbers to improper fractions.

a $2\frac{1}{4}$ 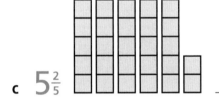 _____

b $4\frac{2}{3}$ _____

c $5\frac{2}{5}$ _____

d $3\frac{5}{6}$ _____

You can use multiplication to do this more quickly.

Example Change $3\frac{5}{6}$ to an improper fraction.

Step 1: multiply the **whole number** by the **denominator**. $3 \times 6 = 18$
(This gives how many sixths there are in the three whole ones.)

Step 2: add on the numerator (the extra sixths). $18 + 5 = 23$
(This gives the numerator of the improper fraction.)

The denominator stays the same.   So $3\frac{5}{6} = \frac{23}{6}$

---

2 Change these mixed numbers to improper fractions.

a $3\frac{4}{5}$ _____   **b** $5\frac{2}{3}$ _____   **c** $5\frac{1}{6}$ _____   **d** $6\frac{4}{5}$ _____

e $5\frac{3}{7}$ _____   **f** $4\frac{5}{9}$ _____   **g** $6\frac{7}{10}$ _____   **h** $4\frac{3}{8}$ _____

Progress test 3

1 Simplify the fraction first to help you answer the question in your head.

a $\dfrac{6}{8}$ of **40** = $\dfrac{\square}{\square}$ of **40** = _____

b $\dfrac{25}{100}$ of **8** = $\dfrac{\square}{\square}$ of **8** = _____

2 Write any equivalent fractions from the box in the correct bags.

$\dfrac{3}{4}$ $\dfrac{2}{3}$ $\dfrac{5}{6}$

$\dfrac{8}{12}$ $\dfrac{6}{9}$

$\dfrac{9}{12}$ $\dfrac{10}{12}$

$\dfrac{15}{18}$ $\dfrac{4}{6}$

$\dfrac{5}{8}$ $\dfrac{6}{8}$

3 Fill in the missing numbers to show equivalent fractions.

a $\dfrac{6}{15} = \dfrac{2}{\square}$

b $\dfrac{14}{16} = \dfrac{\square}{8}$

c $\dfrac{35}{45} = \dfrac{\square}{\square}$

4 Change these fractions so that they have a common denominator.
Circle the largest fraction in each set.

a $\dfrac{2}{3}$ $\dfrac{5}{6}$ $\dfrac{7}{9}$ ____ ____ ____

b $\dfrac{9}{12}$ $\dfrac{7}{8}$ $\dfrac{3}{4}$ ____ ____ ____

5 Change these improper fractions to mixed numbers.

a $\dfrac{5}{2}$ _____

b $\dfrac{9}{4}$ _____

c $\dfrac{17}{6}$ _____

6 Change these mixed numbers to improper fractions.

a $3\dfrac{5}{6}$ _____

b $5\dfrac{3}{4}$ _____

c $7\dfrac{2}{3}$ _____

Adding and subtracting fractions

 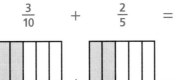
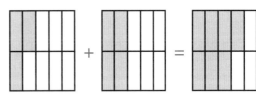
Activities

1 Answer these questions, by first changing one fraction to an equivalent one so that the two
fractions have a common denominator.

a $\frac{4}{9} + \frac{1}{3} =$ _____

b $\frac{1}{4} + \frac{3}{8} =$ _____

c $\frac{3}{10} + \frac{3}{5} =$ _____

d $\frac{1}{12} + \frac{2}{3} =$ _____

e $\frac{8}{9} - \frac{2}{3} =$ _____

f $\frac{11}{12} - \frac{5}{6} =$ _____

g $\frac{9}{10} - \frac{2}{5} =$ _____

h $\frac{6}{7} - \frac{5}{14} =$ _____

2 Add these fractions and give your answers as mixed numbers.

a $\frac{3}{4} + \frac{7}{8} =$ _____

b $\frac{5}{6} + \frac{2}{3} =$ _____

c $\frac{3}{10} + \frac{4}{5} + \frac{1}{10} =$ _____

d $\frac{7}{12} + \frac{1}{6} + \frac{1}{3} =$ _____

Multiplying fractions by whole numbers

Watch what happens when you multiply a fraction by a whole number.

Example At a restaurant three people eat some pizza. Each person eats $\frac{3}{4}$ of a pizza. How much pizza is eaten altogether?

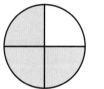

Three lots of three-quarters is nine-quarters. $3 \times \frac{3}{4} = \frac{9}{4}$

The answer can be written as the improper fraction $\frac{9}{4}$ or as a mixed number $2\frac{1}{4}$.

Notice that only the numerator, **3**, is multiplied by the whole number. The denominator stays the same.

Activities

1 Answer these questions, giving your answers as improper fractions.

a $2 \times \frac{3}{5} =$ _____

b $\frac{2}{3} \times 2 =$ _____

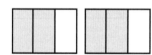

c $\frac{2}{5} \times 3 =$ _____

d $4 \times \frac{4}{7} =$ _____

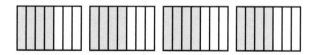

2 Answer these questions, giving your answers as improper fractions.

a $3 \times \frac{3}{5} =$ _____

b $\frac{2}{3} \times 5 =$ _____

c $\frac{2}{9} \times 8 =$ _____

d $6 \times \frac{3}{5} =$ _____

3 Answer these questions, giving your answers as mixed numbers, simplifying if possible.

a $2 \times \frac{5}{7} =$ _____

b $\frac{7}{10} \times 3 =$ _____

c $\frac{5}{6} \times 4 =$ _____

d $6 \times \frac{11}{12} =$ _____

Thousandths

Explanation

Measurements are often split into **1000** equal pieces called **thousandths**.
For example, a kilometre is split into 1000 equal parts called metres.
One metre is **one-thousandth** or $\frac{1}{1000}$ of a kilometre.

Fractions with the denominator **1000** can sometimes be simplified to equivalent fractions.

Example $\frac{200}{1000} = \frac{20}{100} = \frac{1}{5}$ $\qquad$ $\frac{700}{1000} = \frac{70}{100} = \frac{7}{10}$ $\qquad$ $\frac{250}{1000} = \frac{25}{100} = \frac{1}{4}$

Activities

1 Count on in thousandths.

a $\frac{16}{1000}, \frac{17}{1000}, \frac{18}{1000}, \frac{}{1000}, \frac{20}{1000}, \frac{}{1000}, \frac{}{1000}, \frac{}{1000}, \frac{24}{1000}, \frac{25}{1000}, \frac{}{1000}$ ...

b $\frac{294}{1000}, \frac{295}{1000}, \frac{296}{1000}, \frac{}{1000}, \frac{298}{1000}, \frac{}{1000}, \frac{}{1000}, \frac{}{1000}, \frac{302}{1000}, \frac{}{1000}$ ...

2 Write which fraction from activity **1** is equivalent to:

a $\frac{1}{50}$ _____ **b** $\frac{1}{40}$ _____ **c** $\frac{3}{10}$ _____ **d** $\frac{151}{500}$ _____

When a whole number is divided by **1000** the answer can be written as a fraction.

Example $3 \div 1000 = \frac{3}{1000}$ $\qquad$ $227 \div 1000 = \frac{227}{1000}$

If the number being divided is greater than **1000**, the answer will be greater than **1** and can be written as an improper fraction or mixed number.

Example $2150 \div 1000 = \frac{2150}{1000} = 2\frac{150}{1000} = 2\frac{3}{20}$

---

3 Answer these and write your answers as simplified mixed numbers.

a $4200 \div 1000 =$ _____ **b** $2500 \div 1000 =$ _____ **c** $3400 \div 1000 =$ _____

d $3010 \div 1000 =$ _____ **e** $5050 \div 1000 =$ _____ **f** $16\,125 \div 1000 =$ _____

Common denominators and ordering fractions

Explanation

Sometimes you have to change the fractions to a new **common denominator**.

Example Which is larger $\frac{3}{4}$ or $\frac{5}{6}$?

Quarters can't be changed into sixths, so look at both denominators.

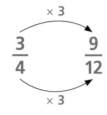 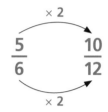

Ask: '*What is the lowest number that* **both 4** *and* **6** *divide into with no remainders?*' The lowest number is **12**. So change both fractions to **equivalent** fractions with the denominator **12**.

$\frac{3}{4}$ ×3 $\frac{9}{12}$ ×3 $\frac{5}{6}$ ×2 $\frac{10}{12}$ ×2

Now you have $\frac{9}{12}$ and $\frac{10}{12}$. As $\frac{10}{12}$ is larger, the answer to the question is $\frac{5}{6}$.

Activities

1 Change both these fractions so they have a common denominator.
Circle the larger fraction in each pair.

a $\frac{2}{3}$ or $\frac{3}{4}$ _____

b $\frac{2}{5}$ or $\frac{3}{8}$ _____

c $\frac{7}{12}$ or $\frac{5}{8}$ _____

Sometimes you need to find a new common denominator for **three** fractions.

Example Put these fractions in order, smallest first: $\frac{5}{6}$, $\frac{7}{8}$ and $\frac{3}{4}$

Ask: '*What is the lowest number that* **6**, **8** *and* **4** *divide into with no remainders?*'

The lowest number is **24**. So change each fraction to an equivalent fraction with a denominator of **24**.

Now you have $\frac{20}{24}$, $\frac{21}{24}$ and $\frac{18}{24}$. In order of size this is $\frac{18}{24}$, $\frac{20}{24}$ and $\frac{21}{24}$.

So the answer to the question is $\frac{3}{4}$, $\frac{5}{6}$ and $\frac{7}{8}$.

2 Put these fractions in order, smallest first, using common denominators.

a $\frac{1}{3}$ $\frac{2}{3}$ $\frac{4}{9}$ _____ _____ _____

b $\frac{5}{8}$ $\frac{1}{4}$ $\frac{3}{4}$ _____ _____ _____

c $\frac{3}{8}$ $\frac{1}{4}$ $\frac{1}{2}$ _____ _____ _____

d $\frac{2}{5}$ $\frac{7}{10}$ $\frac{1}{2}$ _____ _____ _____

e $\frac{1}{2}$ $\frac{2}{3}$ $\frac{5}{8}$ _____ _____ _____

f $\frac{1}{3}$ $\frac{3}{5}$ $\frac{5}{12}$ _____ _____ _____

Simplest form

Explanation

Changing a fraction to its simplest form is sometimes called **reducing to lowest terms** or **cancelling**. It is about finding an equivalent fraction where the numerator and denominator are as small as they can be.

To change a fraction to its simplest form, follow the steps below.

Divide the numerator **and** the denominator by the largest number you can. When you can't divide again by any other number, the fraction is in its **simplest (or lowest) form**. The fractions below have been cancelled to their simplest form.

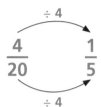 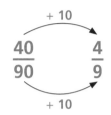 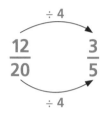

Activities

1 Give these fractions in their simplest form.

a $\frac{30}{90}$ _____

b $\frac{10}{40}$ _____

c $\frac{6}{30}$ _____

d $\frac{9}{45}$ _____

e $\frac{20}{50}$ _____

f $\frac{10}{35}$ _____

g $\frac{8}{20}$ _____

h $\frac{6}{21}$ _____

i $\frac{24}{30}$ _____

j $\frac{42}{56}$ _____

k $\frac{45}{54}$ _____

l $\frac{12}{96}$ _____

2 What fraction of **20** is each of these numbers? Give fractions in their simplest form.

a 10
b 4
c 8
d 5
e 2
f 15

3 What fraction of **50** is each of these numbers? Give fractions in their simplest form.

a 10
b 5
c 20
d 15
e 4
f 36

4 What fraction of **100** is each of these numbers? Give fractions in their simplest form.

a 10
b 5
c 30
d 75
e 55
f 12

Progress test 4

1 Answer these questions.

a $\frac{3}{10} + \frac{2}{5} =$ _____

b $\frac{5}{12} + \frac{2}{3} =$ _____

c $\frac{11}{12} - \frac{3}{4} =$ _____

d $\frac{11}{9} - \frac{2}{3} =$ _____

2 Answer these questions, giving your answers as mixed numbers and simplifying if possible.

a $2 \times \frac{4}{7} =$ _____

b $\frac{9}{10} \times 3 =$ _____

3 Answer these and write your answers as simplified mixed numbers.

a $5800 \div 1000 =$ _____

b $4500 \div 1000 =$ _____

c $11\,200 \div 1000 =$ _____

4 Which is larger?

a $\frac{2}{5}$ or $\frac{1}{2}$ _____

b $\frac{3}{4}$ or $\frac{5}{8}$ _____

c $\frac{5}{12}$ or $\frac{11}{24}$ _____

5 Put these fractions in order, smallest first, by changing them to have a common denominator.

$\frac{3}{4}$ $\frac{2}{3}$ $\frac{5}{6}$ $\frac{5}{8}$ _____ _____ _____ _____

6 Join each of the fractions to their correct place on the number line.

0   1

7 Give these fractions in their simplest form.

a $\frac{70}{80}$ _____

b $\frac{24}{32}$ _____

c $\frac{45}{70}$ _____

Adding fractions and mixed numbers

Explanation

Adding can be done in any order so, when **adding mixed numbers**, the whole numbers can be added together first.

Example $3\frac{3}{10} + 2\frac{4}{5} =$

$3 + 2 + \frac{3}{10} + \frac{4}{5} = 5 + \frac{3}{10} + \frac{4}{5}$

> Change the fractions to have the same denominator.

$= 5 + \frac{3}{10} + \frac{8}{10} = 5 + \frac{11}{10}$

> Don't leave an improper fraction in the answer.

$= 5 + 1\frac{1}{10} = 6\frac{1}{10}$

Activities

1 Answer these, where the fractions in each question have the same denominator.

a $3\frac{1}{9} + \frac{7}{9} =$ _____

b $1\frac{1}{10} + 2\frac{2}{10} =$ _____

c $3\frac{1}{7} + 4\frac{1}{7} =$ _____

d $4\frac{1}{5} + 2\frac{3}{5} =$ _____

2 Answer these, without leaving an improper fraction in the answer.

a $3\frac{4}{5} + 1\frac{2}{5} =$ _____

b $4\frac{3}{8} + 5\frac{7}{8} =$ _____

c $1\frac{9}{10} + \frac{9}{10} =$ _____

d $\frac{7}{12} + 4\frac{11}{12} =$ _____

e $3\frac{3}{4} + 4\frac{3}{4} =$ _____

f $1\frac{7}{9} + 5\frac{8}{9} =$ _____

3 Answer these. You will need to change the fractions to have a common denominator.

a $2\frac{4}{9} + 1\frac{1}{3} =$ _____

b $4\frac{1}{4} + 5\frac{3}{8} =$ _____

c $1\frac{2}{3} + \frac{1}{5} =$ _____

d $\frac{7}{12} + 4\frac{2}{3} =$ _____

e $3\frac{3}{4} + 3\frac{2}{5} =$ _____

f $1\frac{3}{4} + 5\frac{2}{3} =$ _____

Subtracting fractions and mixed numbers

Subtracting mixed numbers can be more difficult than adding since, unlike addition, subtraction cannot be done in any order. Split the second mixed number into a whole number and a fraction and subtract them in two steps.

Example $6\frac{1}{4} - 2\frac{1}{2} =$

$6\frac{1}{4} - 2 - \frac{1}{2} = 4\frac{1}{4} - \frac{1}{2}$

> Change the fractions to have the same denominator.

> It can help to split the second fraction to make the subtraction easier.

$= 4\frac{1}{4} - \frac{2}{4}$

$= 4\frac{1}{4} - \frac{1}{4} - \frac{1}{4} = 4 - \frac{1}{4} = 3\frac{3}{4}$

Activities

1. Answer these, where the fractions in each question have the same denominator and the first fraction is larger than the second.

   a $5\frac{8}{9} - 2\frac{2}{9} =$ _____

   b $7\frac{5}{10} - 2\frac{3}{10} =$ _____

   c $9\frac{6}{7} - 4\frac{4}{7} =$ _____

   d $6\frac{4}{5} - 5\frac{3}{5} =$ _____

2. Answer these, where the fractions in each question have the same denominator, but the second fraction is larger than the first.

   a $7\frac{1}{9} - 2\frac{2}{9} =$ _____

   b $8\frac{1}{10} - 2\frac{3}{10} =$ _____

   c $9\frac{1}{7} - 4\frac{4}{7} =$ _____

   d $7\frac{1}{5} - 1\frac{3}{5} =$ _____

3. Answer these. Change the fractions to have a common denominator.

   a $2\frac{4}{9} - 1\frac{1}{3} =$ _____

   b $8\frac{3}{4} - 5\frac{3}{8} =$ _____

   c $6\frac{5}{8} - 1\frac{3}{4} =$ _____

   d $9\frac{7}{12} - 4\frac{2}{3} =$ _____

   e $8\frac{2}{3} - 1\frac{4}{5} =$ _____

   f $9\frac{7}{10} - 4\frac{4}{5} =$ _____

Fractions

Dividing fractions by whole numbers

Activities

1 Answer these questions.

a $\frac{5}{7} \div 2 =$ _____

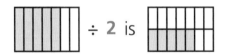 ÷ **2** is

b $\frac{1}{3} \div 4 =$ _____

 ÷ **4** is

c $\frac{3}{4} \div 2 =$ _____

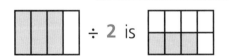 ÷ **2** is

d $\frac{2}{5} \div 3 =$ _____

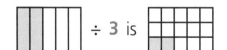 ÷ **3** is

2 Answer these questions.

a $\frac{3}{5} \div 4 =$ _____

b $\frac{2}{3} \div 5 =$ _____

c $\frac{3}{4} \div 7 =$ _____

d $\frac{2}{7} \div 3 =$ _____

3 Answer these questions and simplify your answers.

a $\frac{2}{5} \div 4 =$ _____

b $\frac{4}{7} \div 4 =$ _____

Multiplying pairs of fractions

Activities

1 Answer these questions.

a $\frac{1}{2} \times \frac{5}{7} =$ _____

half of is

b $\frac{1}{2} \times \frac{1}{3} =$ _____

half of is

c $\frac{1}{4} \times \frac{2}{3} =$ _____

quarter of is

d $\frac{2}{3} \times \frac{2}{3} =$ _____

two-thirds of is

2 Answer these questions.

a $\frac{3}{5} \times \frac{3}{5} =$ _____

b $\frac{2}{3} \times \frac{2}{5} =$ _____

c $\frac{3}{4} \times \frac{1}{5} =$ _____

d $\frac{2}{7} \times \frac{3}{5} =$ _____

3 Answer these questions, giving answers in the simplest form.

a $\frac{2}{5} \times \frac{3}{5} =$ _____

b $\frac{5}{6} \times \frac{4}{10} =$ _____

c $\frac{4}{5} \times \frac{5}{8} =$ _____

d $\frac{2}{7} \times \frac{3}{4} =$ _____

Final test

1 Colour the fraction shown.

a $\frac{1}{5}$    b $\frac{3}{8}$    c $\frac{5}{6}$

2 Answer these questions mentally.

a
> A football team played
> **24** matches in a season.
> They won $\frac{1}{6}$ of them.
> How many did they win?

b
> **One-fifth** of the sweets
> in a bag are red. There
> are **30** sweets in the bag.
> How many are red?

3 Write your answers to these divisions, giving a fraction with the denominator **10**.

a $17 \div 10 =$ _____   b $9 \div 10 =$ _____   c $41 \div 10 =$ _____

4 Find:

a $\frac{3}{8}$ of 24 _____   b $\frac{4}{5}$ of 25 _____   c $\frac{4}{9}$ of 36 _____

5 Fill in the missing fractions.

a $1 - \boxed{\frac{7}{8}} = \dfrac{\Box}{\Box}$

b $1 - \boxed{\frac{3}{5}} = \dfrac{\Box}{\Box}$

c $1 - \boxed{\frac{3}{10}} = \dfrac{\Box}{\Box}$

d $1 - \boxed{\frac{7}{9}} = \dfrac{\Box}{\Box}$

6 Add or subtract these fractions, giving your answers as mixed numbers or proper fractions.

a $\frac{7}{10} + \frac{4}{10} =$ _____   b $\frac{8}{9} - \frac{3}{9} =$ _____

c $\frac{8}{10} + \frac{9}{10} =$ _____   d $\frac{27}{7} - \frac{2}{7} =$ _____

7 Write your answers as fractions with the denominator **100**.

a $4 \div 100 =$ _____   b $19 \div 100 =$ _____   c $241 \div 100 =$ _____

8 Join each of the fractions to their correct position on the number line.

$\dfrac{9}{10}$ $\dfrac{1}{2}$ $\dfrac{3}{5}$ $\dfrac{1}{5}$ $\dfrac{3}{10}$

0   **1**

9 Write these fractions in order, smallest first.

$\dfrac{3}{5}$ $\dfrac{3}{10}$ $\dfrac{1}{5}$ $\dfrac{1}{2}$ $\dfrac{7}{10}$ _____   _____   _____   _____   _____

10 Write these fractions in order, largest first.

$\dfrac{7}{12}$ $\dfrac{3}{4}$ $\dfrac{1}{2}$ $\dfrac{1}{3}$ $\dfrac{5}{6}$ _____   _____   _____   _____   _____

11 Compare these fractions, writing <, > or = between them.

a $\dfrac{3}{10}$ _____ $\dfrac{1}{5}$ **b** $\dfrac{5}{8}$ _____ $\dfrac{3}{4}$ **c** $\dfrac{2}{6}$ _____ $\dfrac{1}{3}$

d $\dfrac{2}{9}$ _____ $\dfrac{1}{3}$ **e** $\dfrac{3}{12}$ _____ $\dfrac{1}{4}$ **f** $\dfrac{9}{12}$ _____ $\dfrac{3}{4}$

12 Order these fractions, smallest first.

a $\dfrac{2}{10}$ $\dfrac{1}{10}$ $\dfrac{7}{10}$ _____   **b** $\dfrac{4}{5}$ $\dfrac{3}{5}$ $\dfrac{2}{5}$ _____

c $\dfrac{4}{7}$ $\dfrac{3}{7}$ $\dfrac{1}{7}$ _____   **d** $\dfrac{1}{8}$ $\dfrac{3}{8}$ $\dfrac{5}{8}$ _____

e $\dfrac{1}{3}$ $\dfrac{1}{8}$ $\dfrac{1}{5}$ _____   **f** $\dfrac{1}{10}$ $\dfrac{1}{9}$ $\dfrac{1}{6}$ _____

13 Simplify the fraction first to help you answer the question in your head.

a $\boxed{\dfrac{2}{8}}$ of **12** = $\dfrac{\square}{\square}$ of **12** = _____

b $\boxed{\dfrac{3}{6}}$ of **26** = $\dfrac{\square}{\square}$ of **26** = _____

c $\boxed{\dfrac{8}{10}}$ of **35** = $\dfrac{\square}{\square}$ of **35** = _____

d $\boxed{\dfrac{9}{12}}$ of **16** = $\dfrac{\square}{\square}$ of **16** = _____

14 Add these fractions and give your answers as mixed numbers.

a $\dfrac{3}{4} + \dfrac{7}{8} =$ _____

b $\dfrac{5}{6} + \dfrac{2}{3} =$ _____

c $\dfrac{3}{10} + \dfrac{4}{5} + \dfrac{2}{5} =$ _____

d $\dfrac{7}{12} + \dfrac{1}{6} + \dfrac{1}{4} =$ _____

15 Change these improper fractions to mixed numbers.

a $\dfrac{33}{10}$ _____

b $\dfrac{11}{5}$ _____

c $\dfrac{17}{12}$ _____

d $\dfrac{25}{6}$ _____

e $\dfrac{13}{3}$ _____

f $\dfrac{19}{4}$ _____

16 Change these mixed numbers to improper fractions.

a $3\frac{4}{5}$ _____

b $4\frac{1}{10}$ _____

c $5\frac{5}{6}$ _____

17 Write each of these fractions in its simplest form.

a $\dfrac{30}{100}$ _____

b $\dfrac{24}{30}$ _____

c $\dfrac{8}{40}$ _____

d $\dfrac{7}{28}$ _____

e $\dfrac{48}{72}$ _____

f $\dfrac{18}{54}$ _____

18 Answer these questions, giving your answers as improper fractions.

a $3 \times \frac{3}{5} =$ _____

b $\frac{3}{4} \times 2 =$ _____

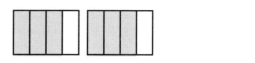

19 Answer these and write your answers as simplified mixed numbers.

a $6800 \div 1000 =$ _____

b $2400 \div 1000 =$ _____

c $13\,500 \div 1000 =$ _____

20 Which is larger?

a $\frac{3}{8}$ or $\frac{2}{5}$ _____

b $\frac{3}{10}$ or $\frac{2}{3}$ _____

c $\frac{6}{8}$ or $\frac{5}{6}$ _____

d $\frac{2}{3}$ or $\frac{5}{7}$ _____

21 Answer these. Change the fractions to have a common denominator.

a $4\frac{4}{9} + 3\frac{1}{3} =$ _____

b $2\frac{1}{4} + 1\frac{3}{8} =$ _____

c $5\frac{4}{9} - 2\frac{1}{3} =$ _____

d $7\frac{3}{8} - 4\frac{3}{4} =$ _____

22 Answer these questions and simplify your answers.

a $\frac{2}{5} \div 6 =$ _____

b $\frac{4}{5} \div 8 =$ _____

23 Answer these questions and simplify your answers.

a $\frac{2}{5} \times \frac{5}{6} =$ _____

b $\frac{5}{9} \times \frac{3}{10} =$ _____

Answers to Activities

Page 5: Unit fractions of shapes

1 **a** $\frac{1}{6}$ **b** $\frac{1}{6}$ **c** $\frac{1}{8}$ **d** $\frac{1}{9}$

  e $\frac{1}{4}$ **f** $\frac{1}{3}$ **g** $\frac{1}{4}$

2 **a, b, c** One segment should be coloured in each shape.

3 **a** ✗ **b** ✓ **c** ✗

  d ✗ **e** ✗ **f** ✓

Page 6: Unit fractions of numbers

1 **a** 4 **b** 3

2 **a** 3 **b** 5

  c 5 **d** 4

3 **a** £6 **b** 6 **c** 20 **d** 20

Page 7: Fractions that are several parts of a whole

1 **a** $\frac{5}{6}$ **b** $\frac{1}{2}$ or $\frac{3}{6}$ **c** $\frac{5}{8}$ **d** $\frac{4}{9}$

  e $\frac{3}{4}$ **f** $\frac{2}{3}$ **g** $\frac{3}{4}$

2 **a** 5 segments coloured

  b 2 segments coloured

  c 7 segments coloured

  d 3 segments coloured

  e 2 segments coloured

  f 4 segments coloured

3 **b** and **c** should be ticked.

Page 8: Fractions of sets

1 **a** $\frac{5}{8}$ **b** $\frac{4}{9}$

  c $\frac{5}{12}$ **d** $\frac{11}{15}$

  e $\frac{3}{8}$ **f** $\frac{9}{11}$

2 **a** 3 smileys coloured

  b 7 cans coloured

  c 5 stars coloured

  d 5 hearts coloured

3 **b** and **d** should be ticked.

Page 9: Mixed numbers

1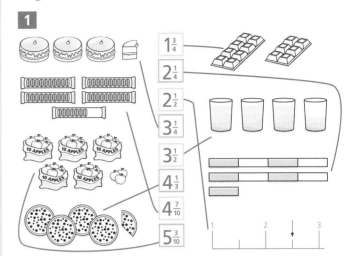

2 **a** 3, $3\frac{1}{2}$, 4, $4\frac{1}{2}$, 5, $5\frac{1}{2}$

  b $1\frac{1}{2}$, $1\frac{3}{4}$, 2, $2\frac{1}{4}$, $2\frac{1}{2}$, $2\frac{3}{4}$

  c $4\frac{2}{3}$, 5, $5\frac{1}{3}$, $5\frac{2}{3}$, 6, $6\frac{1}{3}$

  d $1\frac{2}{5}$, $1\frac{3}{5}$, $1\frac{4}{5}$, 2, $2\frac{1}{5}$, $2\frac{2}{5}$

Page 10: Equivalent fractions 1

1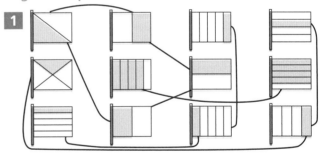

2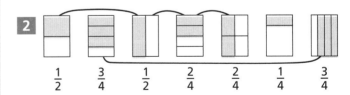

$\frac{1}{2}$ $\frac{3}{4}$ $\frac{1}{2}$ $\frac{2}{4}$ $\frac{2}{4}$ $\frac{1}{4}$ $\frac{3}{4}$

Page 11: Finding fractions of numbers

1 **a** 8 **b** 12 **c** 12 **d** 15

2 **a** 6 **b** 9 **c** 28 **d** 25

  e 30 **f** 30 **g** 21 **h** 56

3 **a** 18 **b** 24 **c** 36 **d** 45

4 **a** 24 **b** 32 **c** 20 **d** 36

5 **a** 6 hours **b** 5 hours **c** 9 hours **d** 4 hours

Page 13: Tenths

1 **a** $\frac{5}{10}, \frac{6}{10}, \frac{8}{10}, \frac{13}{10}, \frac{14}{10}$

b $1\frac{3}{10}, 1\frac{4}{10}, 1\frac{6}{10}, 1\frac{7}{10}, 1\frac{8}{10}, 1\frac{9}{10}, 2$

2 **a** $\frac{1}{10}$ **b** $\frac{9}{10}$ **c** $\frac{6}{10}$

d $\frac{2}{10}$ **e** $\frac{4}{10}$ **f** $\frac{8}{10}$

3 **c** is $\frac{3}{5}$, **d** is $\frac{1}{5}$, **e** is $\frac{2}{5}$, **f** is $\frac{4}{5}$

Page 14: Fractions with a total of one

1 The following pairs are written in any order:

$\frac{1}{6} + \frac{5}{6}$ $\frac{5}{8} + \frac{3}{8}$

$\frac{1}{2} + \frac{1}{2}$ $\frac{1}{7} + \frac{6}{7}$

$\frac{1}{4} + \frac{3}{4}$ $\frac{2}{5} + \frac{3}{5}$

$\frac{3}{10} + \frac{7}{10}$ $\frac{9}{10} + \frac{1}{10}$

$\frac{7}{8} + \frac{1}{8}$ $\frac{1}{9} + \frac{8}{9}$

$\frac{4}{9} + \frac{5}{9}$ $\frac{1}{5} + \frac{4}{5}$

$\frac{3}{7} + \frac{4}{7}$

Page 15: Adding fractions with the same denominators

1 **a** $\frac{7}{9}$ **b** $\frac{7}{8}$

c $\frac{9}{10}$ **d** $\frac{5}{7}$

2 **a** $\frac{13}{10}$ **b** $\frac{12}{9}$

c $\frac{10}{7}$ **d** $\frac{10}{8}$

3 **a** $1\frac{1}{4}$ **b** $1\frac{2}{5}$

c $1\frac{3}{10}$ **d** $1\frac{6}{9}$ or $1\frac{2}{3}$

e $2\frac{3}{10}$ **f** $1\frac{5}{6}$

Page 16: Subtracting fractions with the same denominators

1 **a** $\frac{7}{9}$ **b** $\frac{2}{8}$

c $\frac{6}{10}$ **d** $\frac{4}{7}$

2 **a** $\frac{8}{7}$ **b** $\frac{12}{5}$

c $\frac{13}{10}$ **d** $\frac{19}{6}$

3 **a** $1\frac{1}{4}$ **b** $1\frac{4}{5}$

c $1\frac{7}{10}$ **d** $1\frac{4}{7}$

Page 17: Comparing and ordering unit fractions

1 **a** >   **b** <   **c** >

d <   **e** >   **f** >

2 **a** $\frac{1}{8}, \frac{1}{5}, \frac{1}{2}$ **b** $\frac{1}{10}, \frac{1}{9}, \frac{1}{3}$

c $\frac{1}{9}, \frac{1}{4}, \frac{1}{3}$ **d** $\frac{1}{10}, \frac{1}{8}, \frac{1}{6}$

3 **a** $\frac{1}{4}, \frac{1}{6}, \frac{1}{7}, \frac{1}{9}$

b $\frac{1}{2}, \frac{1}{5}, \frac{1}{7}, \frac{1}{10}$

c $\frac{1}{2}, \frac{1}{4}, \frac{1}{5}, \frac{1}{9}$

Page 18: Ordering fractions

1 **a** >   **b** <   **c** >

d <   **e** >   **f** >

2 **a** $\frac{1}{5}, \frac{3}{5}, \frac{4}{5}$ **b** $\frac{1}{8}, \frac{3}{8}, \frac{6}{8}$

c $\frac{4}{9}, \frac{6}{9}, \frac{7}{9}$ **d** $\frac{1}{10}, \frac{2}{10}, \frac{9}{10}$

3 **a** $\frac{9}{12}, \frac{7}{12}, \frac{5}{12}, \frac{3}{12}$

b $\frac{7}{10}, \frac{5}{10}, \frac{4}{10}, \frac{3}{10}$

c $\frac{6}{8}, \frac{4}{8}, \frac{2}{8}, \frac{1}{8}$

Page 19: Equivalent fractions 2

1 **a** 3 parts and 7 parts shaded; $\frac{7}{8}$ is larger

  b 1 part and 1 part shaded; $\frac{1}{4}$ is larger

  c 2 parts and 4 parts shaded; they are equivalent

  d 3 parts and 5 parts shaded; $\frac{5}{6}$ is larger

  e 2 parts and 6 parts shaded; $\frac{6}{8}$ is larger

  f 3 parts and 9 parts shaded; they are equivalent

2 **a** $\frac{2}{3}, \frac{4}{6}$ **b** $\frac{12}{15}, \frac{4}{5}$ **c** $\frac{3}{4}, \frac{9}{12}$

  d $\frac{6}{8}, \frac{12}{16}$ **e** $\frac{1}{5}, \frac{3}{15}$ **f** $\frac{6}{10}, \frac{9}{15}$

Page 20: Fraction wall

1 **a** =   **b** >   **c** =

  d >   **e** =   **f** =

  g =   **h** =   **i** =

Page 21: Hundredths

1 **a** $\frac{5}{100}, \frac{6}{100}, \frac{7}{100}, \frac{8}{100}, \frac{9}{100}, \frac{12}{100}, \frac{13}{100}$

  b $\frac{49}{100}, \frac{50}{100}, \frac{51}{100}, \frac{52}{100}, \frac{53}{100}, \frac{56}{100}, \frac{57}{100}$

  c $1\frac{2}{100}, 1\frac{3}{100}, 1\frac{5}{100}, 1\frac{6}{100}, 1\frac{7}{100}, 1\frac{8}{100}, 1\frac{9}{100}$

2 **a** $\frac{1}{100}$ **b** $\frac{29}{100}$ **c** $\frac{9}{100}$

  d $\frac{70}{100}$ **e** $\frac{75}{100}$ **f** $\frac{50}{100}$

3 **d** is $\frac{7}{10}$, **e** $= \frac{3}{4}$, **f** is $\frac{1}{2}$

Page 23: Simplifying fractions 1

1 **a** $\frac{1}{4}$, 5   **b** $\frac{1}{2}$, 11

  c $\frac{4}{5}$, 20   **d** $\frac{3}{4}$, 30

  e $\frac{2}{3}$, 20   **f** $\frac{3}{5}$, 21

2 **a** $\frac{7}{10}$, 21 **b** $\frac{9}{10}$, 18 **c** $\frac{3}{10}$, 27 **d** $\frac{7}{10}$, 84

Page 24: Fractions on a number line

1 **a**

  b

  c

2 **a** $\frac{1}{9}, \frac{1}{3}, \frac{5}{9}, \frac{2}{3}, \frac{7}{9}$

  b $\frac{1}{12}, \frac{1}{6}, \frac{2}{6}, \frac{5}{12}, \frac{7}{12}, \frac{2}{3}, \frac{5}{6}$

Page 25: Equivalent fractions 3

1 Sets are written in any order:

$\frac{1}{2}$ $\frac{5}{10}$ $\frac{6}{12}$ $\frac{5}{10}$ $\frac{50}{100}$

$\frac{3}{8}$ $\frac{6}{16}$

$\frac{5}{6}$ $\frac{10}{12}$ $\frac{15}{18}$

$\frac{1}{4}$ $\frac{2}{8}$ $\frac{4}{16}$

$\frac{4}{10}$ $\frac{2}{5}$ $\frac{8}{20}$ $\frac{16}{40}$

$\frac{1}{5}$ $\frac{3}{15}$ $\frac{4}{20}$ $\frac{5}{25}$ $\frac{2}{10}$

$\frac{1}{7}$ $\frac{2}{14}$

$\frac{1}{3}$ $\frac{2}{6}$ $\frac{10}{30}$ $\frac{5}{15}$ $\frac{3}{9}$ $\frac{4}{12}$

2 Two more equivalent fractions for each set are written.

Page 26: Simplifying fractions 2

1 **a** $\frac{1}{4}$ **b** $\frac{1}{2}$ **c** $\frac{4}{5}$

  d $\frac{7}{10}$ **e** $\frac{2}{3}$ **f** $\frac{2}{6}$

2 Answers may vary but should be equivalent to the one shown each time.

  a $\frac{1}{5}$ **b** $\frac{3}{4}$ **c** $\frac{5}{7}$

  d $\frac{2}{3}$ **e** $\frac{2}{9}$ **f** $\frac{7}{8}$

Page 27: Common denominators

1 Two fractions equivalent, for example:

a $\frac{6}{10}$ or $\frac{9}{15}$ **b** $\frac{10}{16}$ or $\frac{50}{80}$ **c** $\frac{2}{3}$ or $\frac{60}{90}$

d $\frac{5}{7}$ or $\frac{20}{28}$ **e** $\frac{4}{5}$ or $\frac{8}{10}$ **f** $\frac{3}{10}$ or $\frac{15}{50}$

2 Answers may vary.

a $\frac{4}{10}$, $\frac{3}{10}$; $\frac{2}{5}$ is larger

b $\frac{2}{8}$, $\frac{3}{8}$; $\frac{3}{8}$ is larger

c $\frac{10}{16}$, $\frac{11}{16}$; $\frac{11}{16}$ is larger

d $\frac{6}{9}$, $\frac{5}{9}$; $\frac{2}{3}$ is larger

e $\frac{9}{24}$, $\frac{11}{24}$; $\frac{11}{24}$ is larger

f $\frac{12}{21}$, $\frac{11}{21}$; $\frac{4}{7}$ is larger

3 **a** $\frac{7}{9}$ **b** $\frac{13}{16}$ **c** $\frac{5}{6}$

Page 28: Mixed numbers and improper fractions 1

1 **a** $1\frac{1}{2}$ **b** $3\frac{1}{2}$ **c** $1\frac{2}{3}$ **d** $1\frac{3}{4}$

    e $1\frac{7}{10}$ **f** $2\frac{3}{5}$ **g** $2\frac{5}{6}$ **h** $5\frac{1}{4}$

    i $6\frac{1}{4}$ **j** $4\frac{2}{5}$ **k** $7\frac{5}{6}$ **l** $5\frac{9}{10}$

Page 29: Mixed numbers and improper fractions 2

1 **a** $\frac{9}{4}$ **b** $\frac{14}{3}$

    c $\frac{27}{5}$ **d** $\frac{23}{6}$

2 **a** $\frac{19}{5}$ **b** $\frac{17}{3}$ **c** $\frac{31}{6}$ **d** $\frac{34}{5}$

    e $\frac{38}{7}$ **f** $\frac{41}{9}$ **g** $\frac{67}{10}$ **h** $\frac{35}{8}$

Page 31: Adding and subtracting fractions

1 Some fractions could also be simplified.

a $\frac{7}{9}$ **b** $\frac{5}{8}$

c $\frac{9}{10}$ **d** $\frac{9}{12}$

e $\frac{2}{9}$ **f** $\frac{1}{12}$

g $\frac{5}{10}$ **h** $\frac{7}{14}$

2 Some fractions could also be simplified.

a $1\frac{5}{8}$ **b** $1\frac{3}{6}$

c $1\frac{2}{10}$ **d** $1\frac{1}{12}$

Page 32: Multiplying fractions by whole numbers

1 **a** $\frac{6}{5}$ **b** $\frac{4}{3}$

    c $\frac{6}{5}$ **d** $\frac{16}{17}$

2 **a** $\frac{9}{5}$ **b** $\frac{10}{3}$

    c $\frac{16}{9}$ **d** $\frac{18}{5}$

3 **a** $1\frac{3}{7}$ **b** $2\frac{1}{10}$

    c $3\frac{1}{3}$ **d** $5\frac{1}{2}$

Page 33: Thousandths

1 **a** $\frac{19}{1000}$, $\frac{21}{1000}$, $\frac{22}{1000}$, $\frac{23}{1000}$, $\frac{26}{1000}$

    b $\frac{297}{1000}$, $\frac{299}{1000}$, $\frac{300}{1000}$, $\frac{301}{1000}$, $\frac{303}{1000}$

2 **a** $\frac{20}{1000}$ **b** $\frac{25}{1000}$ **c** $\frac{300}{1000}$ **d** $\frac{302}{1000}$

3 **a** $4\frac{1}{5}$ **b** $2\frac{1}{2}$ **c** $3\frac{2}{5}$

    d $3\frac{1}{100}$ **e** $5\frac{1}{20}$ **f** $16\frac{1}{8}$

Page 34: Common denominators and ordering fractions

1 a $\frac{8}{12}$, $\frac{9}{12}$; $\frac{3}{4}$ is larger

  b $\frac{16}{40}$, $\frac{15}{40}$; $\frac{2}{5}$ is larger

  c $\frac{14}{24}$, $\frac{15}{24}$; $\frac{5}{8}$ is larger

2 a $\frac{1}{3}$, $\frac{4}{9}$, $\frac{2}{3}$ b $\frac{1}{4}$, $\frac{5}{8}$, $\frac{3}{4}$

  c $\frac{1}{4}$, $\frac{3}{8}$, $\frac{1}{2}$ d $\frac{2}{5}$, $\frac{1}{2}$, $\frac{7}{10}$

  e $\frac{1}{2}$, $\frac{5}{8}$, $\frac{2}{3}$ f $\frac{1}{3}$, $\frac{5}{12}$, $\frac{3}{5}$

Page 35: Simplest form

1 a $\frac{1}{3}$ b $\frac{1}{4}$ c $\frac{1}{5}$ d $\frac{1}{5}$

  e $\frac{2}{5}$ f $\frac{2}{7}$ g $\frac{2}{5}$ h $\frac{2}{7}$

  i $\frac{4}{5}$ j $\frac{3}{4}$ k $\frac{5}{6}$ l $\frac{1}{8}$

2 a $\frac{1}{2}$ b $\frac{1}{5}$ c $\frac{2}{5}$ d $\frac{1}{4}$ e $\frac{1}{10}$ f $\frac{3}{4}$

3 a $\frac{1}{5}$ b $\frac{1}{10}$ c $\frac{2}{5}$ d $\frac{3}{10}$ e $\frac{2}{25}$ f $\frac{18}{25}$

4 a $\frac{1}{10}$ b $\frac{1}{20}$ c $\frac{3}{10}$ d $\frac{3}{4}$ e $\frac{11}{20}$ f $\frac{3}{25}$

Page 37: Adding fractions and mixed numbers

1 a $3\frac{8}{9}$ b $3\frac{3}{10}$

  c $7\frac{2}{7}$ d $6\frac{4}{5}$

2 a $5\frac{1}{5}$ b $10\frac{2}{8}$ or $10\frac{1}{4}$

  c $2\frac{8}{10}$ or $2\frac{4}{5}$ d $5\frac{6}{12}$ or $5\frac{1}{2}$

  e $8\frac{2}{4}$ or $8\frac{1}{2}$ f $7\frac{6}{9}$ or $7\frac{2}{3}$

3 a $3\frac{7}{9}$ b $9\frac{5}{8}$

  c $1\frac{13}{15}$ d $5\frac{3}{12}$ or $5\frac{1}{4}$

  e $7\frac{3}{20}$ f $7\frac{5}{12}$

Page 38: Subtracting fractions and mixed numbers

1 a $3\frac{6}{9}$ or $3\frac{2}{3}$ b $5\frac{2}{10}$ or $5\frac{1}{5}$

  c $5\frac{2}{7}$ d $1\frac{1}{5}$

2 a $4\frac{8}{9}$ b $5\frac{8}{10}$ or $5\frac{4}{5}$

  c $4\frac{4}{7}$ d $5\frac{3}{5}$

3 a $1\frac{1}{9}$ b $3\frac{3}{8}$

  c $4\frac{7}{8}$ d $4\frac{11}{12}$

  e $6\frac{13}{15}$ f $4\frac{9}{10}$

Page 39: Dividing fractions by whole numbers

1 a $\frac{5}{14}$ b $\frac{1}{12}$

  c $\frac{3}{8}$ d $\frac{2}{15}$

2 a $\frac{3}{20}$ b $\frac{2}{15}$

  c $\frac{3}{28}$ d $\frac{2}{21}$

3 a $\frac{1}{10}$ b $\frac{1}{7}$

Page 40: Multiplying pairs of fractions

1 a $\frac{5}{14}$ b $\frac{1}{6}$ c $\frac{2}{12}$ or $\frac{1}{6}$ d $\frac{4}{9}$

2 a $\frac{9}{25}$ b $\frac{4}{15}$ c $\frac{3}{20}$ d $\frac{6}{35}$

3 a $\frac{6}{25}$ b $\frac{1}{3}$ c $\frac{1}{2}$ d $\frac{3}{14}$

Answers to Progress tests

PROGRESS TEST 1 – Page 12

1 a $\frac{3}{5}$ b $\frac{3}{8}$ c $\frac{2}{7}$ d $\frac{3}{4}$

2 a 4   b 3
   c 4   d 5

3 a £4   b 9
   c 10   d 30

4 a 3 cans coloured
   b 5 hearts coloured
   c 1 smiley coloured

5 a $4\frac{1}{2}$, 5, $5\frac{1}{2}$, 6, $6\frac{1}{2}$, 7
   b $5\frac{1}{2}$, $5\frac{3}{4}$, 6, $6\frac{1}{4}$, $6\frac{1}{2}$, $6\frac{3}{4}$
   c $8\frac{1}{4}$, 8, $7\frac{3}{4}$, $7\frac{1}{2}$, $7\frac{1}{4}$, 7

6 a 12   b 20   c 10

PROGRESS TEST 2 – Page 22

1 a $\frac{7}{10}$ b $\frac{9}{10}$ c $\frac{11}{10}$ or $1\frac{1}{10}$

2 a $\frac{5}{8}$ b $\frac{3}{5}$
   c $\frac{4}{9}$ d $\frac{5}{12}$

3 a $1\frac{3}{10}$ b $1\frac{5}{9}$
   c $2\frac{1}{10}$ d $3\frac{1}{8}$

4 a $\frac{1}{8}$, $\frac{1}{4}$, $\frac{1}{2}$ b $\frac{1}{12}$, $\frac{2}{12}$, $\frac{9}{12}$

5 $\frac{1}{2}$ and $\frac{4}{8}$ joined, $\frac{4}{12}$ and $\frac{1}{3}$ and $\frac{2}{6}$ joined

6 $\frac{79}{100}$, $\frac{80}{100}$, $\frac{81}{100}$, $\frac{82}{100}$, $\frac{85}{100}$, $\frac{86}{100}$

7 a $\frac{7}{100}$ b $\frac{51}{100}$ c $\frac{273}{100}$ or $2\frac{73}{100}$

PROGRESS TEST 3 – Page 30

1 a $\frac{3}{4}$, 30   b $\frac{1}{4}$, 2

2 $\frac{3}{4}$, $\frac{6}{8}$, $\frac{9}{12}$
   $\frac{2}{3}$, $\frac{4}{6}$, $\frac{8}{12}$, $\frac{6}{9}$
   $\frac{5}{6}$, $\frac{10}{12}$, $\frac{15}{18}$

3 a $\frac{2}{5}$ b $\frac{7}{8}$ c $\frac{7}{9}$

4 a $\frac{12}{18}$, $\frac{15}{18}$, $\frac{14}{18}$; $\frac{5}{6}$ is largest
   b $\frac{18}{24}$, $\frac{21}{24}$, $\frac{18}{24}$; $\frac{7}{8}$ is largest

5 a $2\frac{1}{2}$ b $2\frac{1}{4}$ c $2\frac{5}{6}$

6 a $\frac{23}{6}$ b $\frac{23}{4}$ c $\frac{23}{3}$

PROGRESS TEST 4 – Page 36

1 a $\frac{7}{10}$ b $1\frac{1}{12}$ or $\frac{13}{12}$
   c $\frac{2}{12}$ or $\frac{1}{6}$ d $\frac{5}{9}$

2 a $1\frac{1}{7}$ b $2\frac{7}{10}$

3 a $5\frac{4}{5}$ b $4\frac{1}{2}$ c $11\frac{1}{5}$

4 a $\frac{1}{2}$ b $\frac{3}{4}$ c $\frac{11}{24}$

5 $\frac{18}{24}$, $\frac{16}{24}$, $\frac{20}{24}$, $\frac{15}{24}$ so in order $\frac{5}{8}$, $\frac{2}{3}$, $\frac{3}{4}$, $\frac{5}{6}$

6

7 a $\frac{7}{8}$ b $\frac{3}{4}$ c $\frac{9}{14}$

Answers to Final test

1   **a**   1 segment coloured

     b   3 segments coloured

     c   5 segments coloured

2   **a**   4   **b**   6

3   **a** $\frac{17}{10}$ or $1\frac{7}{10}$ **b** $\frac{9}{10}$ **c** $\frac{41}{10}$ or $4\frac{1}{10}$

4   **a**   9   **b**   20   **c**   16

5   **a** $\frac{1}{8}$ **b** $\frac{2}{5}$

     c $\frac{7}{10}$ **d** $\frac{2}{9}$

6   **a** $1\frac{1}{10}$ **b** $\frac{5}{9}$

     c $1\frac{7}{10}$ **d** $3\frac{4}{7}$

7   **a** $\frac{4}{100}$ **b** $\frac{19}{100}$ **c** $\frac{241}{100}$ or $2\frac{41}{100}$

8

9 $\frac{1}{5}, \frac{3}{10}, \frac{1}{2}, \frac{3}{5}, \frac{7}{10}$

10 $\frac{5}{6}, \frac{3}{4}, \frac{7}{12}, \frac{1}{2}, \frac{1}{3}$

11   **a**   >   **b**   <   **c**   =

     d   <   **e**   =   **f**   =

12   **a** $\frac{1}{10}, \frac{2}{10}, \frac{7}{10}$ **b** $\frac{2}{5}, \frac{3}{5}, \frac{4}{5}$

     c $\frac{1}{7}, \frac{3}{7}, \frac{4}{7}$ **d** $\frac{1}{8}, \frac{3}{8}, \frac{5}{8}$

     e $\frac{1}{8}, \frac{1}{5}, \frac{1}{3}$ **f** $\frac{1}{10}, \frac{1}{9}, \frac{1}{6}$

13   **a** $\frac{1}{4}$, 3   **b** $\frac{1}{2}$, 13

     c $\frac{4}{5}$, 28   **d** $\frac{3}{4}$, 12

14   **a** $1\frac{5}{8}$ **b** $1\frac{3}{6}$ or $1\frac{1}{2}$

     c $1\frac{5}{10}$ or $1\frac{1}{2}$ **d** $\frac{12}{12}$ or 1

15   **a** $3\frac{3}{10}$ **b** $2\frac{1}{5}$ **c** $1\frac{5}{12}$

     d $4\frac{1}{6}$ **e** $4\frac{1}{3}$ **f** $4\frac{3}{4}$

16   **a** $\frac{19}{5}$ **b** $\frac{41}{10}$ **c** $\frac{35}{6}$

17   **a** $\frac{3}{10}$ **b** $\frac{4}{5}$ **c** $\frac{1}{5}$

     d $\frac{1}{4}$ **e** $\frac{2}{3}$ **f** $\frac{1}{3}$

18   **a** $\frac{9}{5}$ **b** $\frac{6}{4}$

19   **a** $6\frac{4}{5}$ **b** $2\frac{2}{5}$ **c** $13\frac{1}{2}$

20   **a** $\frac{2}{5}$ **b** $\frac{2}{3}$

     c $\frac{5}{6}$ **d** $\frac{5}{7}$

21   **a** $7\frac{7}{9}$ **b** $3\frac{5}{8}$

     c $3\frac{1}{9}$ **d** $2\frac{5}{8}$

22   **a** $\frac{1}{15}$ **b** $\frac{1}{10}$

23   **a** $\frac{1}{3}$ **b** $\frac{1}{6}$